NONFICTION Phonics Readers

This *My Little Workbook* belongs to

your name

Written by Liza Charlesworth
Design by Cynthia Ng
Photos ©: Getty Images and Shutterstock.com.

ISBN 978-1-339-02798-2

Scholastic Inc., 557 Broadway, New York, NY 10012

First printing, August 2023.
PO#5100144

1 2 3 4 5 6 7 8 9 10 68 32 31 30 29 28 27 26 25 24 23

Contents

Dear Learner:

This *My Little Workbook* is here to give you extra practice with long vowels, digraphs, and more. Turn to it each time you read a book in your *Nonfiction Phonics Readers* set. Filling in the prompts and doing the activities will help you become a super-strong reader, writer, and speller.

Happy Learning,
Your Friends at Scholastic

Complete the sentence.

Chimp chums can

____.
chimp activity

Add *ch* or *-ch* to make words. Then, read each one aloud.

1. _____imp
2. su_____
3. _____op
4. bran_____
5. _____amp
6. mun_____
7. _____omp
8. mu_____
9. _____ums
10. _____ick

Complete the sentence.

This is a shell fact:

____.
shell fact

Add *sh* or -*sh* to make words. Then, read each one aloud.

1. ______ell
2. fi______
3. ______ip
4. ru______
5. ______ut
6. swi______
7. hu______
8. ______op
9. ca______
10. ______ack

Complete the sentence.

This is a moth fact:

____.
moth fact

Add *th* or *-th* to make words. Then, read each one aloud.

1. mo_____
2. _____is
3. _____ick
4. _____umb
5. _____at
6. pa_____
7. _____em
8. wi_____
9. _____en
10. _____e

digraph: *wh*

Complete the sentence.

When it is hot, I like to

____.

summer activity

Add *wh* to make words. Then, read each one aloud.

1. _____en
2. _____ack
3. _____iff
4. _____am
5. _____iz
6. _____im
7. _____ich
8. _____ip
9. _____ale
10. _____at

Complete the sentence.

These things are pink:

____.

pink animals and/or objects

Say each word then find it in the puzzle.

thing sing song long pink sink thank honk dunk drink

y	t	h	i	n	g	x	l	o	n	g	q	s	i	n	k
r	d	r	i	n	k	r	u	z	e	t	s	i	n	g	o
t	h	a	n	k	z	e	h	o	n	k	d	w	a	z	x
d	u	n	k	u	s	o	n	g	p	i	c	p	i	n	k

long a: a_e

Complete the sentence.

This is a whale fact:

____.
whale fact

Say each word then find it in the puzzle.

whale wave game cage chase same lake take brave race

c	a	g	e	g	b	o	r	a	g	q	b	r	a	v	e
r	w	h	a	l	e	d	u	c	h	a	s	e	q	u	g
t	s	a	m	e	q	i	t	a	k	e	d	g	a	m	e
r	a	c	e	u	d	l	a	k	e	e	w	a	v	e	z

long *e*: *e_e*

Complete the sentence.

Pete the pug can ______________.
dog activity

Choose the right word to complete each sentence.

Pete Eve Zeke these Steve

1. This book is about a pug named __________.
2. Pete's pal that begins with E is __________.
3. Pete's pal that begins with Z is __________.
4. Are __________ dog pals fun? Yes!
5. Last, Pete rests on the bed of __________.

long *i*: *i_e*

Complete the sentence.

In class, I like to

____.

favorite school activity

Say each word then find it in the puzzle.

time like ride shine five dine slide hide chime rise

c	h	i	m	e	g	d	i	n	e	z	r	i	s	e	g
q	h	i	d	e	z	r	i	d	e	a	s	h	i	n	e
t	s	l	i	k	e	i	t	o	t	i	m	e	x	e	k
r	f	i	v	e	l	u	d	v	s	l	i	d	e	z	d

long o: o_e

Complete the sentence.

____ ____________________ is a home
A/An — type of animal home

for ____________________.
animal that lives there / plural

Say each word then find it in the puzzle.

home bone hole chose poke dome stone mole whole globe

b	o	n	e	z	s	t	o	n	e	g	c	d	o	m	e
r	p	o	k	e	z	a	g	l	o	b	e	d	u	w	r
m	o	l	e	b	g	l	u	z	w	h	o	l	e	k	v
x	h	o	l	e	b	c	h	o	s	e	v	h	o	m	e

Complete the sentence.

A mule can help by

____.

mule activity

Say each word then find it <u>twice</u> in the puzzle.

mule use cute huge cube fume

o	u	s	e	t	c	u	b	e	o	m	u	l	e	b	x
r	a	c	u	b	e	r	m	u	l	e	g	c	u	t	e
u	s	e	b	f	u	m	e	w	h	u	g	e	q	i	v
r	c	u	t	e	l	h	u	g	e	a	f	u	m	e	z

long *a*: *ai*, *ay*

Complete the sentence.

When it rains, I like to

____.

rain activity

Say each word then find it in the puzzle.

rain sail pail snails day jay bay gray play stay

o	d	a	y	l	j	a	y	x	s	n	a	i	l	s	z
g	r	a	y	u	z	s	a	i	l	e	g	b	a	y	e
u	s	q	p	l	a	y	m	e	w	p	a	i	l	o	v
r	a	i	n	e	l	v	o	s	t	a	y	a	v	m	e

Complete the sentence.

This is a bee fact:

____.
bee fact

Say each word then find it in the puzzle.

neat mean leaf treat cream bees see need meet queen

o	m	e	a	n	e	r	s	e	e	x	l	e	a	f	c
c	r	e	a	m	z	n	e	e	d	e	q	u	e	e	n
u	m	e	e	t	a	y	m	e	n	e	a	t	w	p	a
s	a	q	b	e	e	s	e	l	t	r	e	a	t	v	o

Complete the sentence.

At night, you might see

____.

something you see at night / plural

Say each word then find it in the puzzle.

tries cries flies high might sight flight bright tight fright

s	i	g	h	t	e	m	i	g	h	t	f	l	i	e	s
c	b	r	i	g	h	t	w	f	l	i	g	h	t	o	d
u	g	t	i	g	h	t	a	w	f	r	i	g	h	t	a
t	r	i	e	s	o	c	r	i	e	s	u	h	i	g	h

Complete the sentence.

This is a boat fact:

____.

boat fact

Say each word then find it in the puzzle.

boat floats foam load coast row slow flow snow blow

r	o	w	z	e	f	o	a	m	t	f	l	o	a	t	s
n	z	b	l	o	w	m	i	s	l	o	w	r	i	b	u
q	l	o	a	d	w	l	i	c	f	l	o	w	a	w	t
b	o	a	t	h	s	n	o	w	e	z	c	o	a	s	t

long *u*: *ew, ue*

Complete the sentence.

Jay chicks can ______________________.

jay chick activity

Say each word then find it <u>twice</u> in the puzzle.

new few flew grew due true

f	e	w	q	i	n	e	w	m	t	f	c	o	d	u	e
n	z	f	l	e	w	m	t	r	u	e	w	f	e	w	u
q	d	u	e	o	f	l	e	w	l	g	r	e	w	t	a
g	r	e	w	h	s	t	r	u	e	z	c	u	n	e	w

soft *c*

Complete the sentence.

Mice are nice because

____.

why mice are nice

Say each word then find it in the puzzle.

nice mice twice slice dice race place space face cent

t	w	i	c	e	x	u	k	o	s	l	i	c	e	a	r
n	d	i	c	e	w	r	a	c	e	v	z	c	e	n	t
s	p	a	c	e	a	f	a	c	e	l	n	i	c	e	g
g	n	p	m	i	c	e	d	t	p	l	a	c	e	y	j

Complete the sentence.

A job I might like is:

____.
possible job

Say each word then find it in the puzzle.

cage page stage wage huge badge bridge fudge judge

t	h	u	g	e	x	j	u	d	g	e	c	p	a	g	e
n	c	a	g	e	w	r	b	a	d	g	e	p	y	e	v
b	r	i	d	g	e	f	a	c	b	l	s	t	a	g	e
g	c	e	w	a	g	e	c	e	f	u	d	g	e	y	j

suffix: *-ing*

Complete the sentence.

A big cat can ______________________.

big cat activity

Change the meaning of each word by adding *-ing*.

1. creep = creeping
2. leap = ____________
3. eat = ____________
4. float = ____________
5. peek = ____________
6. play = ____________
7. dash = ____________
8. dream = ____________
9. sleep = ____________
10. drink = ____________

Complete the sentence.

A fun way to get fit is:

____.
fitness activity

Turn each word into a contraction.

1. I will = I'll
2. he will = ________
3. she will = ________
4. we will = ________
5. they will = ________
6. he will = ________
7. they will = ________
8. I will = ________
9. she will = ________
10. we will = ________

Complete the sentence.

An insect can ____________________.
insect activity

Choose the right word to complete each sentence.

pumpkin upset basket insects hidden

1. This book is about ____________________.
2. A picnic lunch is in the ____________________.
3. The green insect on the leaf is ____________________.
4. You can make a face on a ____________________.
5. An insect landed on a kid,
but he was not ____________________.

Complete the sentence.

A fact about reptiles is:

____.
reptile fact

Choose the right word to complete each sentence.

beneath mistake reptiles except display

1. This book is about ______________.
2. Reptiles have 4 legs ______________ for snakes.
3. Reptiles can ______________ spikes.
4. A reptile can hide ______________ rocks.
5. If you dislike reptiles, it is a ______________.

Complete the sentence.

In the sunshine, I like to

____.

sunny-day activity

Choose the right word to complete each sentence.

sailboat milkshake backpack sunshine sandbox

1. This book is about bright ____________.
2. You can float in a ____________.
3. You can lug things in a ____________.
4. It's nice to drink a ____________.
5. It's fun to dig in a ____________.

review

Complete the sentence.

In a cave, you might see

____.

something in a cave / plural

Choose the right word to complete each sentence.

sleep cave upside insects bright

1. This book is about life in a ______________.
2. A cave is not light or ______________.
3. A cave is a safe place for a cub to ______________.
4. Bats hang ______________ down.
5. A cave is a home for snakes and ______________.

review

Complete the sentence.

In a tree, you might see

______________________________________.

something in a tree / plural

Choose the right word to complete each sentence.

tree slide sloth gibbon ribbit

1. This book is about life in a ________________.
2. Snakes hiss, slip, and ________________.
3. A frog says, "________________!"
4. An animal that sleeps a lot is a ________________.
5. An ape that leaps in trees is a ________________.

review

Complete the sentence.

In the sea, you might spot

____.

something in a sea / plural

Choose the right word to complete each sentence.

whale snapshots play eel sea

1. This book is about the deep ______________.
2. A long thin fish is an ______________.
3. A humpback is a huge ______________.
4. Seals flip and ______________.
5. The man in the book takes ______________.

Answer Key

Page 5 / Chimps Can Be Chums

1. chimp **2.** such **3.** chop
4. branch **5.** champ
6. munch **7.** chomp
8. much **9.** chums **10.** chick

Page 6 / Pick Up a Shell

1. shell **2.** fish **3.** ship **4.** rush
5. shut **6.** swish **7.** hush
8. shop **9.** cash **10.** shack

Page 7 / This Moth

1. moth **2.** this **3.** thick
4. thumb **5.** that **6.** path
7. them **8.** with
9. then **10.** the

Page 8 / When It Is Hot

1. when **2.** whack **3.** whiff
4. wham **5.** whiz **6.** whim
7. which **8.** whip **9.** whale
10. what

Page 9 / Pink Things

y t h i n g x l o n g q s i n k
r d r i n k r u z e t s i n g o
t h a n k z e h o n k d w a z x
d u n k u s o n g p i c p i n k

Page 10 / A Whale Can Wave

c a g e g b o r a g q b r a v e
r w h a l e d u c h a s e q u g
t s a m e q i t a k e d g a m e
r a c e u d l a k e e w a v e z

Page 11 / A Pug Named Pete

1. Pete **2.** Eve **3.** Zeke
4. these **5.** Steve

Page 12 / Class Time

c h i m e g d i n e z r i s e g
q h i d e z r i d e a s h i n e
t s l i k e i t o t i m e x e k
r f i v e l u d v s l i d e z d

Page 13 / That Is a Home

b o n e z s t o n e g c d o m e
r p o k e z a g l o b e d u w r
m o l e b g l u z w h o l e k v
x h o l e b c h o s e v h o m e

Page 14 / A Mule Can Help

o u s e t c u b e o m u l e b x
r a c u b e r m u l e g c u t e
u s e b f u m e w h u g e q i v
r c u t e l h u g e a f u m e z

Page 15 / Rain Day

o d a y l j a y x s n a i l s z
g r a y u z s a i l e g b a y e
u s q p l a y m e w p a i l o v
r a i n e l v o s t a y a v m e

Page 16 / A Bee Is Neat!

o m e a n e r s e e x l e a f c
c r e a m z n e e d e q u e e n
u m e e t a y m e n e a t w p a
s a q b e e s e l t r e a t v o

Page 17 / At Night

s i g h t e m i g h t f l i e s
c b r i g h t w f l i g h t o d
u g t i g h t a w f r i g h t a
t r i e s o c r i e s u h i g h

Page 18 / Row a Boat

r o w z e f o a m t f l o a t s
n z b l o w m i s l o w r i b u
q l o a d w l i c f l o w a w t
b o a t h s n o w e z c o a s t

Page 19 / The New Chicks

f e w q i n e w m t f c o d u e
n z f l e w m t r u e w f e w u
q d u e o f l e w l g r e w t a
g r e w h s t r u e z c u n e w

Page 20 / Nice, Nice Mice

t w i c e x u k o s l i c e a r
n d i c e w r a c e v z c e n t
s p a c e a f a c e l n i c e g
g n p m i c e s t p l a c e y j

Page 21 / You Can Get a Job

t h u g e x j u d g e c p a g e
n c a g e w r b a d g e p y e v
b r i d g e f a c b l s t a g e
g c e w a g e c e f u d g e y j

Page 22 / Creeping and Leaping

1. creeping **2.** leaping
3. eating **4.** floating
5. peeking **6.** playing
7. dashing **8.** dreaming
9. sleeping **10.** drinking

Page 23 / We'll Get Fit

1. I'll **2.** he'll **3.** she'll **4.** we'll
5. they'll **6.** he'll **7.** they'll
8. I'll **9.** she'll **10.** we'll

Page 24 / This Insect

1. insects **2.** basket **3.** hidden
4. pumpkin **5.** upset

Page 25 / Reptile Facts

1. reptiles **2.** except **3.** display
4. beneath **5.** mistake

Page 26 / Sunshine Is Fine

1. sunshine **2.** sailboat
3. backpack **4.** milkshake
5. sandbox

Page 27 / Life in a Cave

1. cave **2.** bright **3.** sleep
4. upside **5.** insects

Page 28 / High in a Tree

1. tree **2.** slide **3.** ribbit
4. sloth **5.** gibbon

Page 29 / Deep in the Sea

1. sea **2.** eel **3.** whale
4. play **5.** snapshots

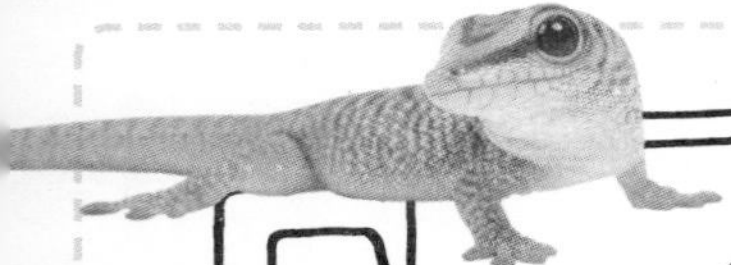

CONGRATULATIONS!

____

your name

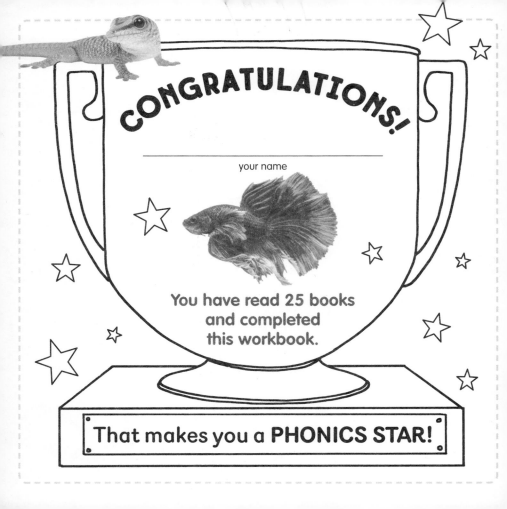

You have read 25 books and completed this workbook.

That makes you a **PHONICS STAR!**